New Framework Maths

Word Problems
Year 4

By Karen Hamilton

RISING ★ STARS

Miss. Thompson.

This book is not photocopiable.

Rising Stars UK Ltd., 22 Grafton Street, London
W1S 4EX

www.risingstars-uk.com

Every effort has been made to trace copyright
holders and obtain their permission for the use of
copyright material. The authors and publishers will
gladly receive information enabling them to rectify
any error or omission in subsequent editions.

All facts are correct at time of going to press.

First edition published 2003
This edition published 2007
Reprinted 2008
Text, design and layout © Rising Stars UK Ltd.
Editorial consultant: Caroline Cooke
Design and illustration: Redmoor Design,
Tavistock, Devon

British Library Cataloguing in Publication Data

A CIP record for this book is available from the
British Library.

ISBN 978-1-84680-215-7

Printed by Craft Print International Ltd., Singapore

Contents

Coverage of Primary National Strategy Objectives

The objective columns (1–16) are listed below the table.

Topic	1	2	3	4	5	6	7	8	9	10	11	12	13	14	15	16
Place value	✓	✓					✓					✓			✓	
Fractions	✓	✓														
Decimals	✓	✓						✓								
Addition and subtraction	✓	✓												✓		
Money	✓	✓						✓				✓		✓	✓	
Time	✓	✓										✓	✓	✓	✓	
Measures – mass	✓	✓		✓				✓				✓	✓	✓	✓	
Measures – capacity	✓	✓			✓			✓			✓	✓	✓	✓	✓	
Measures – length	✓	✓						✓				✓	✓	✓	✓	
Puzzles	✓	✓		✓	✓	✓							✓	✓		
Patterns and sequences					✓	✓										
Multiplication and division	✓	✓				✓							✓	✓		
2D shapes		✓		✓	✓											
3D shapes		✓		✓	✓											
Position and direction		✓	✓	✓												
Data handling			✓													
Two-step problems	✓	✓									✓	✓		✓	✓	
Mixed bag	✓	✓			✓						✓	✓		✓	✓	

Using and applying mathematics

1. Solve one-step and two-step problems involving numbers, money or measures, including time; choose and carry out appropriate calculations, using calculator methods where appropriate
2. Represent a puzzle or problem using number sentences, statements or diagrams; use these to solve the problem; present and interpret the solution in the context of the problem
3. Suggest a line of enquiry and the strategy needed to follow it; collect, organise and interpret selected information to find answers
4. Identify and use patterns, relationships and properties of numbers or shapes; investigate a statement involving numbers and test it with examples
5. Report solutions to puzzles and problems, giving explanations and reasoning orally and in writing, using diagrams and symbols

Counting and understanding number

6. Recognise and continue number sequences formed by counting on or back in steps of constant size
7. Partition, round and order four-digit whole numbers; use positive and negative numbers in context and position them on a number line; state inequalities using the symbols < and > (e.g. $-3 > -5$, $-1 < +1$)
8. Use decimal notation for tenths and hundredths and partition decimals; relate the notation to money and measurement; position one-place and two-place decimals on a number line
9. Recognise the equivalence between decimal and fraction forms of one half, quarters, tenths and hundredths
10. **Use diagrams to identify equivalent fractions (e.g. $\frac{6}{8}$ and $\frac{3}{4}$, or $\frac{7}{100}$ and $\frac{7}{10}$); interpret mixed numbers and position them on a number line (e.g. $3\frac{1}{2}$)**
11. Use the vocabulary of ratio and proportion to describe the relationship between two quantities (e.g. 'There are 2 red beads to every 3 blue beads, or 2 beads in every 5 beads are red'); estimate a proportion (e.g. 'About one quarter of the apples in the box are green')

Knowing and using number facts

12. Use knowledge of addition and subtraction facts and place value to derive sums and differences of pairs of multiples of 10, 100 or 1000
13. Identify the doubles of two-digit numbers; use these to calculate doubles of multiples of 10 and 100 and derive the corresponding halves
14. **Derive and recall multiplication facts up to 10×10, the corresponding division facts and multiples of numbers to 10 up to the tenth multiple**
15. Use knowledge of rounding, number operations and inverses to estimate and check calculations
16. Identify pairs of fractions that total 1

Calculating

Topic	Add or subtract mentally pairs of two-digit whole numbers (e.g. 47 + 58, 91 – 35)	Refine and use efficient written methods to add and subtract two-digit and three-digit whole numbers and £.p	Multiply and divide numbers to 1000 by 10 and then 100 (whole number answers), understanding the effect; relate to scaling up or down	Develop and use written methods to record, support and explain multiplication and division of two-digit numbers by a one-digit number, including division with remainders (e.g. 15 × 9, 98 ÷ 6)	Find fractions of numbers, quantities or shapes (e.g. ⅕ of 30 plums, ⅜ of a 6 by 4 rectangle)	Use a calculator to carry out one-step and two-step calculations involving all four operations; recognise negative numbers in the display, correct mistaken entries and interpret the display correctly in the context of money	Draw polygons and classify them by identifying their properties, including their line symmetry	Visualise 3-D objects from 2-D drawings; make nets of common solids	Recognise horizontal and vertical lines; use the eight compass points to describe direction; describe and identify the position of a square on a grid of squares	Know that angles are measured in degrees and that one whole turn is 360°; compare and order angles less than 180°	Choose and use standard metric units and their abbreviations when estimating, measuring and recording length, weight and capacity; know the meaning of kilo, centi and milli and, where appropriate, use decimal notation to record measurements (e.g. 1.3 m or 0.6 kg)	Interpret intervals and divisions on partially numbered scales and record readings accurately, where appropriate to the nearest tenth of a unit	Draw rectangles and measure and calculate their perimeters, find the area of rectilinear shapes drawn on a square grid by counting squares	Read time to the nearest minute; use am, pm and 12-hour clock notation; choose units of time to measure time intervals; calculate time intervals from clocks and timetables	Answer a question by identifying what data to collect; organise, present, analyse and interpret the data in tables, diagrams, tally charts, pictograms and bar charts, using ICT where appropriate	Compare the impact of representations where scales have intervals of differing step size
Place value			✓													
Fractions					✓											
Decimals					✓											
Addition and subtraction	✓	✓														
Money	✓	✓														
Time	✓	✓												✓		
Measures – mass	✓	✓	✓								✓					
Measures – capacity	✓	✓	✓	✓	✓						✓	✓				
Measures – length	✓	✓	✓	✓							✓	✓	✓			
Puzzles	✓															
Patterns and sequences																
Multiplication and division				✓												
2D shapes							✓									
3D shapes								✓								
Position and direction									✓							
Data handling															✓	
Two-step problems	✓	✓		✓							✓					
Mixed bag	✓	✓		✓												

Column groupings: Understanding shape (Draw polygons … 180°); Measuring (Choose and use … timetables); Handling data (Answer a question … differing step size).

How to use this book

This book is designed to help you use your mathematical skills to solve a range a problems, many of which are written in words rather than figures.

Rather than giving a calculation like:

4 × 6 = ☐

a word problem might be along the lines of:

"If I have 4 six-packs of cola, how many cans of cola do I have in total?"

The answer is the same, but you need to think about it a bit more and remember to answer by writing or saying: "I have 24 cans of cola in total."

The introduction

This section of each page gives you an idea of the sort of problems you are likely to see and helps you to understand what maths you need to use.

Measures - mass

Problems about mass can either be longer 'story'-type problems, which need careful thinking about, or shorter calculation questions. Always remember to put in the units (g, kg).

Asweeni's lunch box weighs 900 g. Sam's lunch box weighs 300 g more. How much does Sam's lunch box weigh?

Read the question then read it again	This is a story question. I need to work out how much Sam's lunch box weighs.
Decide your operations and units	Sam's lunch box weighs 300 g more than Asweeni's. Sounds like addition to me! Remember it's grams though.
Approximate your answer	It's more than 1 kg but less than 1.5 kg. Say, about 1.2 kg.
Calculate	900 g + 300 g = 1200 g. That is 1 kg and 200 g or 1.2 kg.
Check your answer	If we subtract 300 g from 1.2 kg we get 900 g. That's it!

HINTS and TIPS

Remember the following facts:

kilo = 1000   centi = 0.01   milli = 0.001

22

Hints and tips

The hints and tips section gives you useful ideas for completing the problems on the other page. These are the things you need to remember if you are doing a quiz or test!

The example problem

The flow chart takes you through an example problem *step-by-step*. This is important when answering word problems as it helps you to order your thoughts, do each part of the problem in the right order and *check your work*!

Every problem has the same five steps.
READ the question then read it again
DECIDE your operations and units
APPROXIMATE your answer
CALCULATE
CHECK your answer

We remember this by using this mnemonic:

RAIN
DROPS
ARE
CRYSTAL
CLEAR

MEASURES – MASS

Questions

1 (a) How much heavier is 4.5 kg than 800 g?

 1 kg

(b) What is the difference in weight between 600 g and 9 kg?

(c) Asweeni has a pile of 10 books. The pile has a mass of 2 kg. Each book has the same mass. How much does each book weigh?

 400g 200g 400g 400g 100g 300g

2 (a) Asweeni has two bags of weights. They have a total mass of 1800 g. Help Asweeni to share the weights between the two bags so that the mass of one bag is twice that of the other.

(b) Now share the weights between the two bags so that there is a difference of just 200 g.

Challenge

The total is 1000.
Find 10 pairs of numbers that have a total of 1000 g.
They must not be multiples of 2 or 5.

23

The questions

The questions get harder as you go down the page.

- Section 1 questions are fairly straightforward and help you to practise your skills.
- Section 2 questions are a bit harder but will help you to remember all the key points.
- The Challenge sections are really tough and sometimes mean that you can make up games and your own questions! They can be great fun!

All about word problems

Ten top tips for working with word problems

1 *Work step-by-step.* Follow the flow chart.

RAIN	**R**ead the question then read it again
DROPS	**D**ecide your operations and units
ARE	**A**pproximate your answer
CRYSTAL	**C**alculate
CLEAR	**C**heck your answer

2 Always *show your working* or 'method'. This will help you to keep track of what you have done and may help you to get extra marks.

3 Always *include your units* in the answer. If you don't, you won't get full marks.

4 When you first read through a question, *underline important words and numbers.* This will help you to remember the important bits!

5 *Draw a picture to help you.* Sometimes a question is easier if you can 'see' it. Drawing 6 apples can help you if you need to divide them!

6 If the problem has a number of steps, break it down and do *one step at a time.*

7 When you *check your answers*, look at the inverse operation.

8 Sometimes an answer will 'sound right'. Read it out (quietly) and listen. *Does it make sense?*

9 If you are using measurements (grams, litres, cm), make sure that the *units are the same* before you calculate.

10 Once again! *Read the question and check that your solution answers it.*

Place value

Place value questions often ask you to estimate a total or to do an operation with a number such as 10 or 100.

Thomas had to estimate TV viewing figures to the nearest 100. Here are the actual viewing figures:

Cartoon   7,670   Film   10,097   Soap opera   23,956

Read the question then read it again	This is complicated. I have to estimate three different figures. It's best to work systematically.
Decide your operations and units	I am rounding here. Rounding up or down to the nearest 100. That means looking at the 2nd and 3rd digits from the right.
Approximate your answer	It's to the nearest hundred. That means there are two '0's.
Calculate	Cartoon: 7,670 up to 7,700 Film: 10,097 up to 10,100 Soap opera: 23,956 up to 24,000
Check your answer	I have rounded the numbers to the nearest hundred.

HINTS and TIPS

Some place value questions have numbers written in different ways, e.g. 'What is the difference between 235 and two hundred and thirty-six?' It makes the question easier if you write the numbers out in the same way, e.g. 235 and 236.

Questions

1

(a) If Hannah takes 354 away from 1250, will the answer be closest to 1300, 900 or 1000?

(b) Hannah travels 589 km on Monday and 802 km on Tuesday. Is her total journey closest to 300 km, 1400 km or 1200 km?

(c) How many hundreds are there in:

2300?   1500?   4000?

2

(a) Use digits to write the numbers that are 1000 less than:

six thousand, seven hundred and eighty-three

one thousand and ninety-seven

twenty three thousand, two hundred and sixty-six

(b) Which is larger?

i)   500 multiplied by 100   or   5 × 1000

ii) 600 × 10   or   6 groups of 10 000

iii) 5 × 1000   or   2 times 500

Challenge

What is the largest number you can make with these digits?
Now write the number in words.

What is the smallest number you can make with these digits?
Now write the number in words.

Fractions

Problems about fractions usually ask you to find a fraction of a number or to work out what fraction a smaller number is of a bigger number.

Stephanie has 16 pencils. She gives half of them away.

How many does she have left?

Read the question then read it again	Read slowly and carefully. This one is fractions... but also subtraction.
Decide your operations and units	I need to find out what is half of 16, and then take it away from 16. The units are pencils.
Approximate your answer	Half of 16 sounds like 8 to me.
Calculate	$\frac{1}{2}$ of 16 is 8. $16 - 8 = 8$. Stephanie has 8 pencils left.
Check your answer	I can check by dividing 16 by 2 as well. Yes, it's 8 as well!

HINTS and TIPS

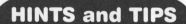

Equivalent fractions can really help with these word problems:

$$\frac{1}{2} = \frac{2}{4} = \frac{3}{6} = \frac{4}{8} = \frac{5}{10} \qquad \frac{1}{5} = \frac{2}{10} = \frac{3}{10} = \frac{4}{20} = \frac{5}{25}$$

$$\frac{1}{4} = \frac{2}{8} = \frac{3}{12} = \frac{4}{16} = \frac{5}{20} \qquad \frac{1}{10} = \frac{2}{20} = \frac{3}{20} = \frac{5}{50} = \frac{10}{100}$$

$$\frac{1}{3} = \frac{2}{6} = \frac{3}{9} = \frac{4}{12} = \frac{5}{15}$$

Questions

1

(a) Stephanie walks $\frac{1}{2}$ a kilometre. How far is this in metres?

(b) $\frac{1}{5}$ of the children in Stephanie's class go home for lunch. There are 30 children in the class. How many go home for lunch?

(c) What fraction of £4 is 50p?

2

(a) There are 12 sweets in a packet. Stephanie gives a quarter of them to Christine and eats $\frac{1}{3}$ of the remaining sweets. How many sweets are left?

(b) Stephanie walks $\frac{2}{5}$ of a kilometre. Christine walks $\frac{3}{10}$ of a kilometre. Who has walked further, Stephanie or Christine? Show your working.

Challenge

Stephanie walks two kilometres on Monday.
The next day she walks half that distance.
Each day she walks half the distance of the previous day.
How far will she have walked in total by Friday?

Decimals

Problems about decimals are usually word stories. Many are about money and sometimes you will have to convert between pounds and pence. Always remember to put the decimal point in!

Daniel has 1.5 m of string. He cuts off 75 cm.

How much string is left?

Read the question then read it again	Read slowly and carefully. The measurements are different units. I will need to convert one.
Decide your operations and units	How much string is left? That's subtraction. Let's keep the units as cm. 1.5 m = 150 cm.
Approximate your answer	It should be between 70 and 80 cm.
Calculate	150 cm – 75 cm = 75 cm There is 75 cm of string left.
Check your answer	Let's check by adding. 75 + 75 = 150. Yes, it's right.

HINTS and TIPS

Always look at the units first with decimal word problems, e.g. cm, m.

If they are different, convert one to make them the same.

Remember to put the decimal point back in at the end!

Questions

1

(a) Daniel spent half of his £23.40 savings. How much did he spend?

(b) What is the difference between 500 ml and 2.7 l?

(c) Daniel has circled the decimal that he thinks is closest to each whole number. Check his work. Record the correct answer.

12 (12.3) 11.1 11.7 11.9

5 (5.6) 7.8 4.7 5.7

34 34.76 (33.95) 33.09 34.67

2

(a) Daniel saves for four days. He is given £10 on Monday. On each of the next three days he gets half the amount of the previous day. How much does he save altogether?

(b) Daniel now saves for another four days. On Monday he gets £1.13 and then he gets double the amount of the previous day for the next three days. How much has he saved this time?

Challenge

You will need one set of digit cards 1–9. Shuffle the cards and choose four digits. Work SYSTEMATICALLY to make as many decimal numbers as you can that have two digits after the decimal point.

Example:

| 2 | 9 | 7 | 3 |

37.92 39.72 32.93
37.29 39.27 32.39

Then place the numbers in each set in numerical order, starting with the smallest number.

15

Addition and subtraction

Addition and subtraction questions can be about anything, so remember to put in the unit or label next to each answer. This can be metres, litres or conkers!

Julia has 132 marbles. She drops her jar and loses 87.

How many marbles does she have now?

Read the question then read it again	Read slowly and carefully. This is about subtraction.
Decide your operations and units	This is subtraction as she 'loses' 87 marbles.
Approximate your answer	Julia has about 130 marbles and loses about 90. The answer should be about 40.
Calculate	132 – 87 = 45 Julia now has 45 marbles.
Check your answer	Check by adding: 45 + 87 = 132. Yes, I'm right!

HINTS and TIPS

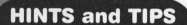

Remember these facts:

When you add	the answer is always
two even numbers	EVEN
two odd numbers	EVEN
an even number and an odd number	ODD

When you subtract	the answer is always
an even number from an even number	EVEN
an odd number from an odd number	EVEN
an even number from an odd number	ODD
an odd number from an even number	ODD

Questions

1

(a) Julia has 43 conkers. Tamara has 58 more. How many conkers does Tamara have?

(b) Julia had 62 stickers. She swapped 35 for a comic. How many stickers does she have now?

(c) Julia scored 138 on level one of her computer game. She scored 297 on level two. What is her total score?

2

(a) 603 spectators attended a football match this week. That is 263 fewer people than attended last week. How many spectators were there last week?

(b) One length of the swimming pool is 25 m. Julia has swum three lengths so far. She is trying to swim 500 m. How many more lengths does she need to swim?

Challenge

Julia buys sheets of 5p and 7p stamps. What totals less than, but close to, 100 can she make? She can use as many of each stamp as she needs to.

Money

Money questions can be adding, subtracting, multiplying or dividing. They also can be about giving or getting change for something.

Solkan spent quarter of his pocket money on a present for his mum. He had £10.

How much did his mum's present cost?

Read the question then read it again	Read slowly and carefully. A quarter is the same as dividing by 4.
Decide your operations and units	This is a division sum. I must remember to put in the £ sign or p if it's pence.
Approximate your answer	$\frac{1}{4}$ of 10 is between 2 and 3.
Calculate	$\frac{1}{4}$ of £10 = 10 ÷ 4 = £2.50. Solkan's mum's present cost £2.50.
Check your answer	Four lots of £2.50 = £10.

HINTS and TIPS

Always remember to put in the £ or p symbols.

There are 100 pence (p) in one pound (£).

Questions

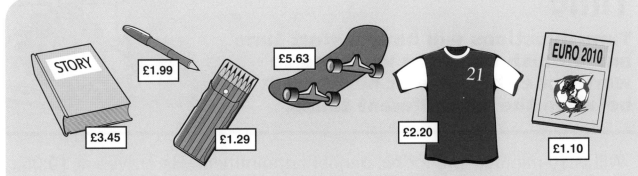

(a) What is the total cost of the least and most expensive items?

(b) Solkan wants to buy two skateboards. How much will they cost?

(c) Solkan has £5. He wants to spend as close to this as possible. Which two items should he buy? How much change would he get?

(a) These are tickets to a theme park. What would be the cheapest price for a family of two adults and four children?

(b) How much would a family of four save if they bought a family ticket rather than individual tickets?

Challenge

Use the items from question 1.
Solkan has £10 to spend. How many different combinations of three items could he buy and still have change?

Time

Time questions will have a start time and a finish time. You will need to work out either time or how long it is between the two different times.

Will is 10 minutes late for his dentist appointment. He arrives at 10:05.

What time should he have arrived?

Read the question then read it again	Read slowly and carefully. Tricky one here. It goes across two different hours.
Decide your operations and units	Subtract 10 minutes from the start time to give the finish time.
Approximate your answer	It will be nearly 10:00 but the time will start with 9.
Calculate	10:05 minus 10 minutes = 9:55. That sounds about right. Will should have arrived at 9:55.
Check your answer	Start at 9:55, add on 10 minutes and I get to 10:05. Correct!

HINTS and TIPS

Watch out for questions about days, weeks, months and years. Remember these facts:

- 60 seconds in a minute
- 60 minutes in an hour
- 24 hours in a day

- 7 days in a week
- 52 weeks in a year
- 12 months in a year

Questions

1

(a) Will arrived 25 minutes late for the start of a pop concert. He arrived at 10 past 8. What time did the concert start?

(b) Will arrives 15 minutes early for the bus. The bus is due to arrive at 9:07. What time was Will at the bus stop?

(c) A film starts at 3:05. It last for 85 minutes. What time does it finish?

2

(a) It takes Keith twice as long as Will to run six kilometres. Will starts at 8:30 and finishes at 9:15. How long does it take Keith to run six kilometres?

(b) Will plays in a five-a-side football tournament. Four matches were played. Each game should have lasted half an hour. Unfortunately, the tournament overran by 25 minutes. The tournament started at 11:30. What time did it finish?

Challenge

Will and Keith's school closes for six weeks on Friday 18th July for the summer holidays. If the school opens on the nearest Monday, when does school re-start for the new school year? Show your working.

Measures - mass

Problems about mass can either be longer 'story'-type problems, which need careful thinking about, or shorter calculation questions. Always remember to put in the units (g, kg).

Asweeni's lunch box weighs 900 g. Sam's lunch box weighs 300 g more.

How much does Sam's lunch box weigh?

Read the question then read it again	This is a story question. I need to work out how much Sam's lunch box weighs.
Decide your operations and units	Sam's lunch box weighs 300 g more than Asweeni's. Sounds like addition to me! Remember it's grams though.
Approximate your answer	It's more than 1 kg but less than 1.5 kg. Say, about 1.2 kg.
Calculate	900 g + 300 g = 1200 g. That is 1 kg and 200 g or 1.2 kg.
Check your answer	If we subtract 300 g from 1.2 kg we get 900 g. That's it!

HINTS and TIPS

Remember the following facts:

kilo = 1000   centi = 0.01   milli = 0.001

Questions

1

(a) How much heavier is 4.5 kg than 800 g?

(b) What is the difference in weight between 600 g and 9 kg?

(c) Asweeni has a pile of 10 books. The pile has a mass of 2 kg. Each book has the same mass. How much does each book weigh?

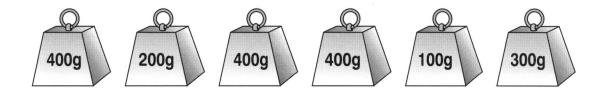

2

(a) Asweeni has two bags of weights. They have a total mass of 1800 g. Help Asweeni to share the weights between the two bags so that the mass of one bag is twice that of the other.

(b) Now share the weights between the two bags so that there is a difference of just 200 g.

Challenge

The total is 1000.
Find 10 pairs of numbers that have a total of 1000 g.
They must not be multiples of 2 or 5.

Measures - capacity

Capacity problems might ask you to work out how many spoons or cups it would take to fill a large bottle or barrel. These are about dividing. You might also need to find out the difference between two capacities.

Selcuk buys a 1 litre bottle of lemonade. He fills a glass and has a drink. There is 700 ml of lemonade left in the bottle.

What is the capacity of the glass?

Read the question then read it again	Read slowly and carefully. I need to find out how much lemonade is in the glass.
Decide your operations and units	I think this is about subtraction. Let's keep the units the same. 1 litre is 1000 ml.
Approximate your answer	10 – 7 = 3
Calculate	1000 ml – 700 ml = 300 ml The capacity of the glass is 300 ml.
Check your answer	I can check by adding. 300 ml + 700 ml = 1000 ml or 1 litre.

HINTS and TIPS

If there are millilitres, centilitres and litres in a question, it helps if you make them all the same unit by multiplying or dividing by 10 or 1000.

millilitres ÷ 1000 = litres   centilitres ÷ 100 = litres
litres × 1000 = millilitres   litres × 100 = centilitres

Questions

1

(a) Selcuk uses four buckets of water to wash a car. Each bucket holds 4 litres. How many litres does he use in total?

(b) Seluck's watering can holds two litres of water. He uses about 200 ml to water one plant. How many plants can he water if he fills the can?

(c) A tin of paint holds 2.5 litres of paint. Selcuk needs 10 litres of paint. How many tins of paint does he need?

2

(a) Selcuk needs 250 ml of water to make a cup of tea. His kettle has a capacity of 1.5 litres. How many cups of tea could he make if he fills and boils the kettle twice?

(b) Selcuk wants to make enough fruit punch to serve five people. How much of each ingredient does he need?

Fruit punch
(serves 3)

1.5 l lemonade
210 ml fruit concentrate
75 ml lemon juice

Challenge

Selcuk has two buckets. One has a capacity of 3 litres and the other has a capacity of 7 litres. Explain how he could use the buckets to measure out 1 litre of liquid.

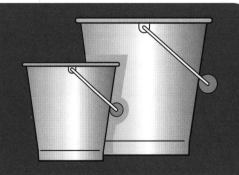

Measures - length

Length questions can be about very short lengths (mm) or huge lengths (miles or km). The problems may be about a journey or measuring something in your home.

On Sports Day Crystal throws the tennis ball 15 m. Jamie throws it 9.5 m.

How much further does Crystal throw the ball?

Read the question then read it again	Read slowly and carefully. I need to find how much further Crystal threw the ball than Jamie.
Decide your operations and units	This is a subtraction question. 'Further than' tells me this. The units are metres.
Approximate your answer	15 – 10 = 5. That should be about right.
Calculate	15 m – 9.5 m = 5.5 m Crystal throws the ball 5.5 m further.
Check your answer	I should check by adding and remember to include my units!

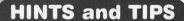

HINTS and TIPS

Remember the relationships between the different units for length:

1000 mm = 1 metre = 100 cm

10 mm = 1 centimetre = $\frac{1}{100}$ metre

Questions

1

(a) Crystal cuts 75 cm from a 4 m roll of ribbon. How much ribbon is left on the roll?

(b) Crystal is 1.25 m tall. Pete is 20 cm taller. How tall is Pete?

(c) Crystal jumped 1 m 90 cm in the sand pit. The winning jump was 2.5 m. How much further did Crystal need to jump to equal the winning jump?

2

(a) Crystal's dad drives from London to Wolverhampton. The journey from London to Wolverhampton is 215 km. How far does he travel if he makes three return trips?

(b) A rectangular playground has a perimeter of 71 m. The length of one side is 15.5 m. What are the lengths of the other sides?

Challenge

I have 3.5 m of rope. I cut it into three pieces. Two pieces are the same length and the third piece is 1.5 m. What is the length of each of the two identical pieces of rope?

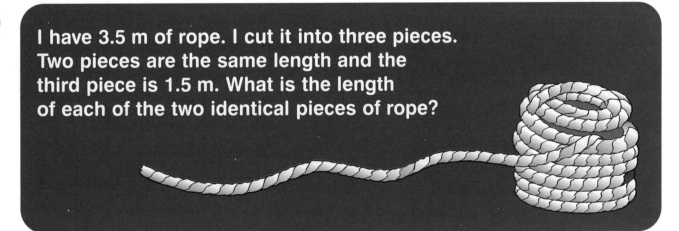

Puzzles

Number puzzles sometimes ask you to look for patterns. They may also ask you to find numbers when you know something about each one, e.g. the sum when they are added or the product when they are multiplied.

Two numbers have a product of 12 and a difference of 1.

What are the two numbers?

Read the question then read it again	This needs careful thought. I am looking for two numbers that are pretty close together.
Decide your operations and units	I need to test my ideas by multiplying and subtracting.
Approximate your answer	This one is too difficult to estimate.
Calculate	Work systematically. What two numbers make 12 when I multiply them? 1 and 12 2 and 6 3 and 4 Now which of those have a difference of one? Easy! 3 and 4.
Check your answer	3 × 4 = 12 4 – 3 = 1 Yes, 3 and 4 satisfy all the rules!

HINTS and TIPS

With puzzles, it is important to think logically. Show your working clearly so that someone else can understand what you have done.

Questions

1

(a) Two numbers have a product of 40 and a difference of 3.
What are they?

(b) Two numbers have a product of 24 and a sum of 10.
What are they?

(c) We are multiples of 3. We are more than 10, but less than 50.
We are also multiples of 4. What numbers are we?

2

(a) Which three consecutive numbers have a sum of 39?
Is it possible for four consecutive numbers to total 39?

(b) The total of two numbers is 18. One number is twice the value
of the other. What are the two numbers?

Challenge

MULTIPLE	FACTOR
PRODUCT	SUM
DIFFERENCE	CONSECUTIVE
MORE THAN	LESS THAN

Use these words to make up two word puzzles for a friend.

Patterns and sequences

Problems involving patterns and sequences usually need you to work out the differences between the numbers.

Special Agent Nigel needs to work out the next three numbers in this sequence to shoot down the giant asteroid that's heading towards us!

He's stuck. Can you help him?

39, 48, 57, 66, ___, ___, ___

Read the question then read it again	'Next three numbers…'
Decide your operations and units	Find the difference between the numbers. That's subtraction.
Approximate your answer	48 − 39 = 9, 57 − 48 = 9, 66 − 57 = 9 The difference is 9.
Calculate	I need to add 9 to find the next three numbers. 66 + 9 = 75, 75 + 9 = 84, 84 + 9 = 93
Check your answer	Double check my answer. Yes, 75, 84 and 93 are the next three numbers in the sequence. Nigel can save the world!

HINTS and TIPS

Practise counting on or back from any number in steps of any single-digit number.

When you've mastered that, try counting on or back in steps of any 2-digit number.

Questions

1

(a) Oh dear, there is more than one asteroid! Nigel needs to guide the missile that will shoot down the second asteroid. Can you help him by working out the next three numbers in this sequence? 46, 39, 32, 25 …

(b) Here comes the next one! Nigel's in trouble again, can you help him? What are the next three numbers?
146, 150, 154, 158 …

(c) That was close! Now Nigel needs you to help him shoot the last asteroid down. Can you work out the next three numbers on his computer display? 247, 244, 241, 238 …

2

(a) Here are two control panels in Nigel's spaceship. Nigel has pressed all the buttons on the first control panel but you need to press all the correct buttons on the next one or the ship will crash! Copy the control panel and shade them in to save the ship.

1	2	3	4	5	6
7	8	9	10	11	12
13	14	15	16	17	18
19	20	21	22	23	24
25	26	27	28	29	30
31	32	33	34	35	36

37	38	39	40	41	42
43	44	45	46	47	48
49	50	51	52	53	54
55	56	57	58	59	60
61	62	63	64	65	66
67	68	69	70	71	72

(b) Nigel says that if he presses button number 110 on a third control panel then the ship will not crash. Should he press it or should you stop him? Explain your answer.

Challenge

Patterns might not always be shown in numbers.
What is the missing letter in this sequence?

J F M A M J __ A S O N D

Multiplication and division

Multiplication and division problems are often set in the kitchen where you have to divide or multiply ingredients. Remember your times tables here!

Remelle buys four packs of bread rolls. Each pack contains six rolls.

How many rolls has he bought?

Read the question then read it again	Read this carefully. What are you being asked to find out?
Decide your operations and units	This is multiplication. 4 packs times 6 rolls.
Approximate your answer	I think it should be 24.
Calculate	$4 \times 6 = 24$ rolls. Remelle has bought 24 rolls.
Check your answer	Check by adding. $6 + 6 + 6 + 6 = 24$. Yes, I'm right!

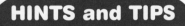

HINTS and TIPS

Remember your written methods for multiplication and division. These can really help!

Questions

1

(a) Remelle buys three dozen eggs. How many eggs does he buy altogether?

(b) Remelle buys five bunches of flowers for his mum. There are nine flowers in each bunch. What is the total number of flowers?

(c) Remelle has 20 marbles. He shares them equally between three friends. How many marbles does each friend get?

2

(a) A pack of 10 batteries costs £3. How much do two batteries cost?

(b) There are eight pencils in a complete set. How many sets can I make using 58 pencils?

Challenge

Remelle exercises every second day. His best friend Selcuk exercises every fifth day.
Start on day 1. When will be the first time that they exercise together? Work out the second, third and fourth times that they will exercise together. What pattern do you notice?

2D shapes

Questions about 2D shapes often ask you to talk about their properties (number of sides, whether sides are equal). Some problems will need you to draw shapes as well.

Draw a polygon with 4 sides, 4 right angles and 2 lines of symmetry.

Read the question then read it again
> Read slowly and carefully. Do I need to draw a picture?

Decide your operations and units
> List the properties: 4 sides, 4 right angles, 2 lines of symmetry.

Approximate your answer
> I think it's a rectangle because a square has 4 lines of symmetry.

Calculate

Check your answer
> Yes, my shape has 4 sides, 4 right angles and 2 lines of symmetry. It's a rectangle!

HINTS and TIPS

Shape work is often about language.
Learn the words to describe shapes, such as:

line, side, edge, vertex, face, base, point, angle, centre and so on.

This will help you to answer questions about all kinds of shapes.

Questions

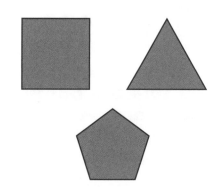

1

(a) Tamara has a bag full of polygons.
   She takes out three.
   The sum of their sides is 12.
   What could the three shapes be?

(b) Tamara has four polygons. There are 16 sides altogether.
   What could the four shapes be? What do you notice about the
   total number of vertices and the total number of angles?

(c) Tamara cuts a shape in half. The two new shapes have a
   total of six sides. What was the original shape? What are
   the new shapes?

2

(a) Sketch the reflection
   of this shape.

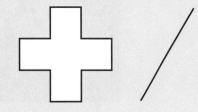

(b) Draw a polygon that has one right angle and at least one
   line of symmetry.

Challenge

Is there a maximum number of right angles that a polygon
can have? Investigate.

3D shapes

Problems about 3D shapes often ask you to work out how many faces, edges and vertices there are.
You might also be asked how many smaller shapes fit into a bigger one.

Name this shape. Then write the names of the shapes of the faces, the number of faces, edges and vertices in the shape.

Read the question then read it again	This question has many parts and lots of information is needed. Put the information in a table.
Decide your operations and units	I need to remember some facts about this shape and count all the different parts of the shape.
Approximate your answer	I think that this is a triangular prism, not a pyramid.
Calculate	Tick off each face, edge and vertex as you count it. Don't forget the faces you can't see! The shapes of the faces are rectangles and triangles.
Check your answer	Check you have been right round the shape.

Shape	Faces	Edges	Vertices
triangular prism	6	12	8

HINTS and TIPS

Keep a note of all the shape names you know with the numbers of faces, edges and vertices next to each shape name.

e.g.

Shape	Faces	Edges	Vertices
cube	6	12	8

Questions

1 Complete this table about polyhedrons.

Name of polyhedron	Shape of faces	Number of faces	Number of edges	Number of vertices
cube				
	square and triangles	5		5
	square and rectangles	6		
hexagonal prism				

2 (a) Christine has a bag full of different polyhedrons. She takes out two shapes. Can you work out what the shapes could be? Here are some clues.

They have: a total of 11 faces;
a total of 20 edges;
a total of 13 vertices.

(b) Christine's baby brother has a toy box.
Its dimensions are: 20 cm by 50 cm by 1 m.
How many 10 cm cubes would he need to fill it?

Challenge

Which of these nets will NOT make a 3D shape? Explain why.

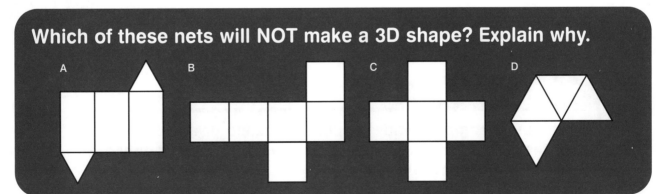

A   B   C   D

Position and direction

Position and direction questions can be about compass directions or finding a point on a grid. The problems can also be about horizontal or vertical lines.

Shanice programs her toy robot Robbie. He starts facing SE then makes a quarter turn clockwise.

Which direction is Robbie facing now?

Read the question then read it again	Read slowly and carefully. Do I need to draw a picture?
Decide your operations and units	The answer is a direction so it should be one of the compass points.
Approximate your answer	A quarter turn to the right should make it SW I think.
Calculate	Draw a compass, then move a quarter of a turn or 90 degrees from SE to SW! Robbie is now facing SW.
Check your answer	A half turn would be NW so, looking back at my answer, SW looks right.

HINTS and TIPS

Sketching a compass with the points labelled or a grid with the points plotted on are good ways of answering these problems systematically.

Questions

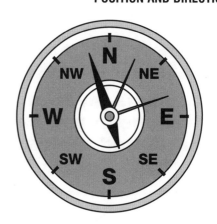

1

(a) Robbie the robot is facing NW. He moves anti-clockwise through a quarter turn. Which direction is he facing now?

(b) Robbie is facing south. He turns clockwise through 45°. Which direction is he facing now?

(c) Robbie is facing east. He turns clockwise through 135°. Which direction is he facing now?

2

(a) Without travelling north, use compass directions to describe the route from A to B to C.

(b) Choose and label three more points, D, E and F. Use compass directions to describe two different routes from D to E to F.

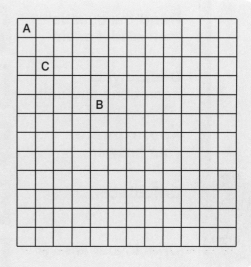

Challenge

Use squared paper. Draw a plan of a garden. Include a path around a fountain in the middle.
Give instructions to a friend for moving around the garden from a starting point that you choose. You can use all eight compass directions. Remember to tell your friend how many squares to move in each direction.

Data handling

Problems involving data handling often mean you have to read graphs, charts and tables accurately.

Trevor was doing a survey of the number of passengers using his local station.
He counted 25 people on the platform at the time of the 1:00 train.

Can you draw the bar on the chart for him?

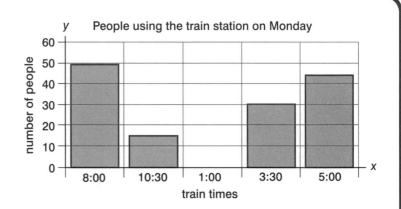

People using the train station on Monday

Read the question then read it again	Read the chart... 25 people... 1:00 train.
Decide your operations and units	I've got to draw a bar on the chart to show 25.
Approximate your answer	The top of the bar mustn't go over 30.
Calculate	Carefully mark the top of the bar, halfway between 20 and 30. Draw in the bar.
Check your answer	Read the completed graph. Yes, my graph is correct.

HINTS and TIPS

Read the title of the graph, chart or table. What is it trying to tell you?

Be careful when reading scales on graphs. Do they go up in 1s, 2s, 5s, 10s or 20s?

Questions

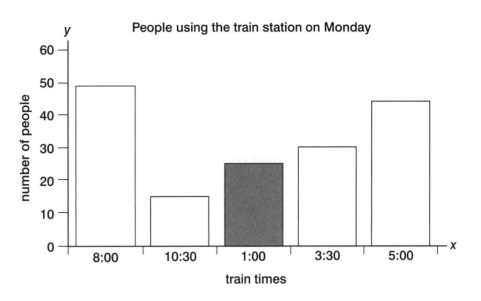

People using the train station on Monday

1 (a) How many people did Trevor count at the time of the 5:00 train?

(b) How many people did Trevor count at the time of the 10:30 train?

(c) On a Monday, which train is most likely to be full?

2 (a) Trevor's results were very similar for Tuesday to Friday. At what times of day do most people use the train from Trevor's local station? Why do you think this is?

(b) How many people did Trevor count in total using the station on Monday?

Challenge

Use squared paper. Can you draw the graph that Trevor might have drawn for people using the station on Sunday?

Two-step problems

**Two-step problems have two steps!
It is important to work out what
each step is asking you to do
before you complete it.**

Ella counts 100 cars in a survey. Half are red, one quarter are blue, and the rest are white.

How many cars were white?

Read the question then read it again	First find out how many cars are red and blue. Then subtract from 100.
Decide your operations and units	The units are cars. Add red and blue cars together then subtract from 100.
Approximate your answer	It is about $\frac{1}{4}$ of 100, so 25
Calculate	$\frac{1}{2}$ of 100 = 50, $\frac{1}{4}$ of 100 = 25 50 + 25 = 75 100 − 75 = 25 25 cars were white.
Check your answer	$\frac{1}{4}$ of 100 = 25. That is right!

HINTS and TIPS

For these problems you need to remain very calm and work through each part of the problem logically.

It is useful to number each step. That will help you.

Questions

1

(a) Ella buys six packets of pencils and five packets of felt-tipped pens. How many pencils and felt-tipped pens does she have altogether?

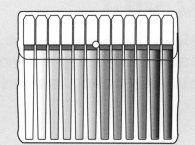

(b) There are 153 books in the class book corner. If 30 children each take home two books, how many books are left in the book corner?

(c) If four cakes cost £2.60, how much would three cakes cost?

2

(a) Ella helps her mum to make coffee for her guests. They need to make 18 cups of coffee. Each cup has a capacity of 250 ml. How many times will they need to fill their kettle, which holds 1.5 litres of water?

(b) What is better value, one bottle or eight cans of Cola?

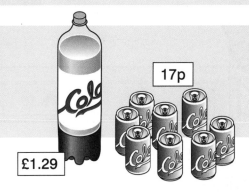

17p

£1.29

Challenge

Two boys get two toys every day for a week.
Three girls get three toys every day for three days.
Who has the most toys, girls or boys?
Explain your working.

Mixed bag

These questions could be about anything! Read them carefully so you understand what you are being asked to do.

Marlon has eight pet spiders. A spider has eight legs.

How many spider legs does Marlon have altogether?

Read the question then read it again	Eight spiders... each spider has eight legs... how many legs?
Decide your operations and units	8 lots of 8. That's multiplication.
Approximate your answer	I know my 8 times table...
Calculate	$8 \times 8 = 64$ Marlon has 64 spider legs.
Check your answer	Have I answered the question? Yes, 64 is correct.

HINTS and TIPS

When you have an answer to a problem, re-read the problem to check you have a sensible answer. Does it look correct?

Questions

1

(a) Ebony thinks of a number. She subtracts 24 and she is left with 18. What was Ebony's number?

(b) Ricky is giving away his collection of 60 comics to five of his best friends. How many comics does each lucky friend receive?

(c) Max has 46 action figures. Josh has half as many again. How many action figures does Josh have?

2

(a) Can you change this recipe for trifle for six people to a recipe for eight people?

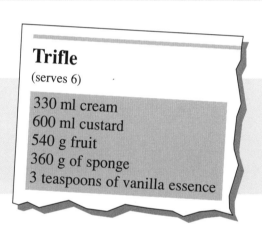

Trifle
(serves 6)

330 ml cream
600 ml custard
540 g fruit
360 g of sponge
3 teaspoons of vanilla essence

(b) The Shoemaker family are off on holiday in their camper van. They drive for 862 miles. Ralph drives for 247 miles and Michael drives for 178 miles. How much further do they have to go?

Challenge

A street that's 30 m long has a horse chestnut tree every 6 m on both sides. How many horse chestnut trees are there along the street?

Answers

Place value

1. (a) 900
   (b) 1400 km
   (c) 23, 15, 40

2. (a) 5783, 97, 22 266
   (b) i) 500 multiplied by 100
      ii) Six groups of 10 000
      iii) 5 × 1000

● Challenge
98 631 or ninety-eight thousand, six hundred and thirty-one
12 589 or twelve thousand, five hundred and eighty-nine

Fractions

1. (a) 500 m
   (b) 6 children
   (c) ⅛

2. (a) 6 sweets
   (b) ⅖ is equivalent to ⁴⁄₁₀, which is more than ³⁄₁₀, so Stephanie has walked furthest.

● Challenge
3 ⅞ kilometres or 3875 metres

Decimals

1. (a) £11.70
   (b) 2.2 l
   (c) 11.9, 4.7, 33.95

2. (a) £18.75   (b) £16.95

● Challenge
Answers will vary.

Addition and subtraction

1. (a) 101   (b) 27   (c) 435

2. (a) 866
   (b) 425 m which is 17 lengths.

● Challenge
Answers will vary but could include:
18 × 5p and 1 × 7p = 97
10 × 5p and 7 × 7p = 99
3 × 5p and 12 × 7p = 99

Money

1. (a) £6.73
   (b) £11.26
   (c) The book and pack of pencils. He will get 26p change.

2. (a) £7.30. £5.50 + 90p + 90p
   (b) 80p

● Challenge
Answers will vary.

Time

1. (a) 7:45   (b) 8:52   (c) 4:30

2. (a) 1½ hours.
   (b) 13:55

● Challenge
1st September.

Measures – mass

1. (a) 3.7 kg   (b) 8.4 kg   (c) 200 g

2. (a) 600 g in one bag and 1200 g in another.
   (b) 1000 g in one bag and 800 g in another.

● Challenge
Answers will vary.

Measures – capacity

1. (a) 16 l
   (b) 10 plants
   (c) 4 tins

2. (a) 12 cups of tea.
   (b) 2.5 l lemonade, 350 ml fruit concentrate, 125 ml lemon juice.

● Challenge
Selcuk should fill the 7 litre bucket first. He should then fill up the 3 litre bucket from the 7 litre bucket and pour that into the sink. He should then fill up the 3 litre bucket from the 7 litre bucket again. What is left in the 7 litre bucket is 1 litre of liquid.

Measures – length

1. (a) 325 cm or 3.25 m
   (b) 1.45 m
   (c) 60 cm

2. (a) 1290 km
   (b) 15.5 m, 20 m, 20 m

● Challenge
1 m

Puzzles

1. (a) 5 and 8
   (b) 6 and 4
   (c) 12, 24, 36, 48

2. (a) 12, 13, 14. There aren't four consecutive numbers that total 39. The closest we can get to it is 38 (8, 9, 10, 11) or 42 (9, 10, 11, 12).
   (b) 6 and 12

● Challenge
Answers will vary.

Patterns and sequences

1 (a) 18, 11, 4
(b) 162, 166, 170
(c) 235, 232, 229

2 (a) Shade in 40, 44, 48, 52, 56, 60, 64, 68, 72
(b) Stop Nigel! The answer does not divide equally by 4, which is the pattern here.

● Challenge
J for July. They are the first letters of the months of the year.

Multiplication and division

1 (a) 36 eggs
(b) 45 flowers
(c) 6 marbles (with 2 left over)

2 (a) 60p
(b) 7 full sets of pencils

● Challenge
They will first exercise together on day 10. They will then exercise together on days 20, 30 and 40. They exercise together every 10 days.

2D shapes

1 (a) Answers will vary but could be square, triangle and pentagon or two rectangles and a square.
(b) Answers will vary but could be two pentagons and two triangles or four rectangles. The total number of vertices is 16 and the total number of angles is 16. 16 is also the total number of sides.
(c) The original shape is a triangle. The new shapes are triangles. Alternative answer: The original shape is a quadrilateral (cut diagonally). The new shapes are triangles.

2 (a)

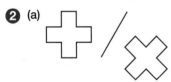

(b) Answers will vary.

● Challenge
Answers will vary.

3D shapes

1

Name of polyhedron	Shape of faces	Number of faces	Number of edges	Number of vertices
cube	square	6	12	8
square-based pyramid	square and triangles	5	8	5
cuboid	square and rectangles	6	12	8
hexagonal prism	hexagons and rectangles	8	18	12

2 (a) A square-based pyramid and a cube or cuboid
(b) 100 cubes

● Challenge
C and D will not make a 3D shape.
C needs another square to make a cube.
D needs a square to make a square-based pyramid.

Position and direction

1 (a) South west
(b) South west
(c) South west

2 (a) Go east 4 squares, then south 4 squares, then north west 2 squares, then west 1 square.
(b) Answers will vary.

● Challenge
Answers will vary.

Data handling

1 (a) 44–45
(b) 14–15
(c) The 8 o'clock train.

2 (a) Most people use the train in the mornings (8:00) and evenings (5:00) when they are going to and coming back from work.
(b) 160–165

● Challenge
Answers will vary but the graph should show fewer people using the train in the morning and evening than on week days.

Two-step problems

1 (a) 36 pencils and 60 pens = 96
(b) 93 books
(c) £1.95

2 (a) 3 times
(b) One bottle

● Challenge
The boys

Mixed bag

1 (a) 42
(b) 12 comics each
(c) 69 action figures

2 (a) 440 ml cream, 800 ml custard, 720 g fruit, 480 g of sponge, 4 teaspoons of vanilla essence.
(b) 437 miles

● Challenge
12 horse chestnut trees